NEIL A. KJOS
PIANO LIBRARY

LEVEL FIVE

PIANO REPERTOIRE

SELECTED & EDITED BY

Keith Snell

Romantic & 20th Century

THE NEIL A. KJOS PIANO LIBRARY

The **Neil A. Kjos Piano Library** is a comprehensive series of piano music in a wide variety of musical styles. The library is divided into eleven levels and will provide students with a complete performance experience in both solo and ensemble music. Teachers will find the carefully graded levels appropriate when choosing repertoire for evaluations, auditions, festivals, and examinations. Included in the **Neil A. Kjos Piano Library:**

Preparatory Level - Level Ten

Fundamentals of Piano Theory
Piano Repertoire: Baroque & Classical
Piano Repertoire: Romantic & 20th Century
Piano Repertoire: Etudes
Scale Skills
Essential Piano Repertoire
Music of the 21st Century
New Age Piano
Jazz Piano
One Piano Four Hands
Music for Christmas

PREFACE

Piano Repertoire: Romantic & 20th Century from the **Neil A. Kjos Piano Library** provides piano students with carefully chosen collections of piano music from the 19th and 20th centuries. Each volume contains an ample selection of music featuring a large assortment of composers and styles. The appropriately graded levels ensure steady and thorough progress as pianists advance in their study of Romantic and 20th Century keyboard literature.

Compact disc recordings are available for each volume in the *Piano Repertoire* series. Recorded by pianist Diane Hidy, the interpretations follow the editions closely as practical examples for students. Each CD includes all three volumes from the *Piano Repertoire* series at each level: *Baroque & Classical, Romantic & 20th Century*, and *Etudes*.*

*Preparatory and Level One are included on one CD.

CONTENTS

ISBN 0-8497-6230-8

Waltz
Op. 9, No. 1

Franz Schubert
(1797-1828)

Waltz
Op. 33, No. 7

Franz Schubert
(1797-1828)

Harmony of the Angels

Op. 100, No. 21

Friedrich Burgmüller
(1806-1874)

Knight Ruppert

Op. 68, No. 12

Robert Schumann
(1810-1856)

Fine

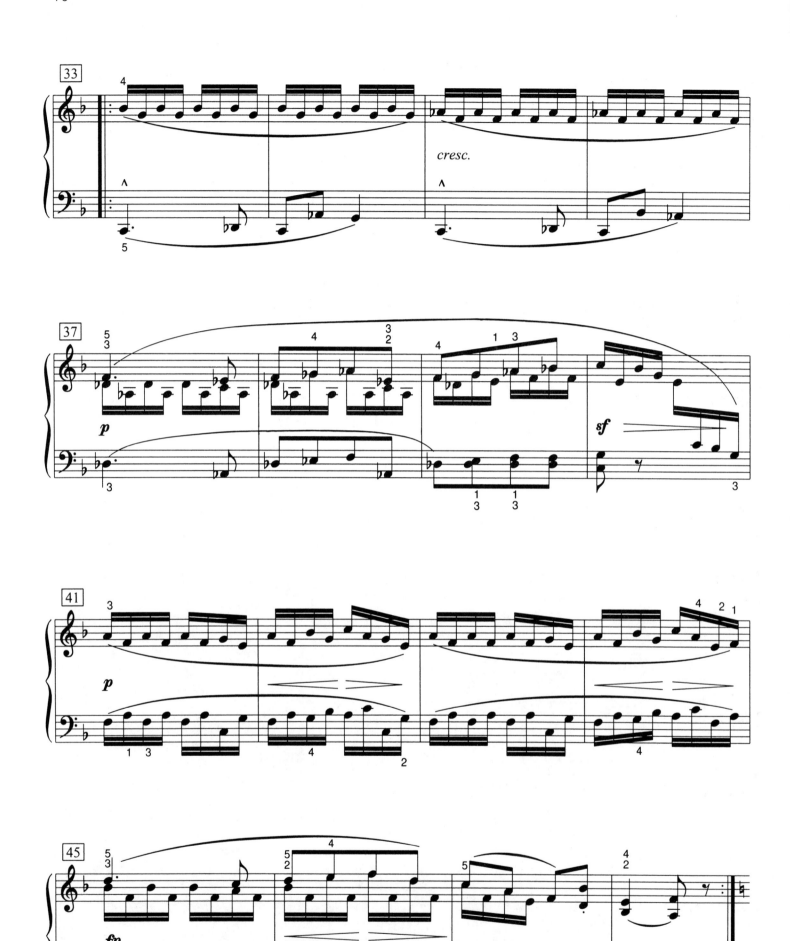

D. C. senza repetizione al Fine

Mazurka

Op. 68, No. 3

Frédéric Chopin
(1810-1849)

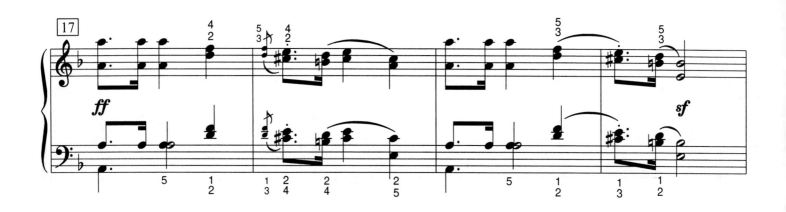

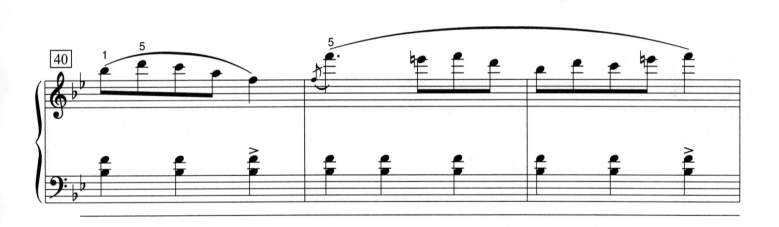

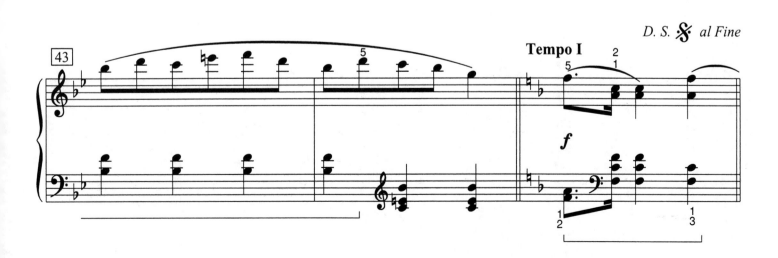

Prelude

Op. 28, No. 7

Frédéric Chopin
(1810-1849)

Grandmother's Minuet

Op. 68, No. 2

Allegretto grazioso e leggierissimo

Edvard Grieg
(1843-1907)

GP625

Sailor's Song

Op. 68, No. 1

Edvard Grieg
(1843-1907)

Italian Song

Op. 39, No. 15

Peter Ilyich Tchaikovsky
(1840-1893)

© 1997 Neil A. Kjos Music Company, 4380 Jutland Drive, San Diego, California, 92117.

Mazurka

Op. 39, No. 10

Peter Ilyich Tchaikovsky
(1840-1893)

Tempo di Mazurka

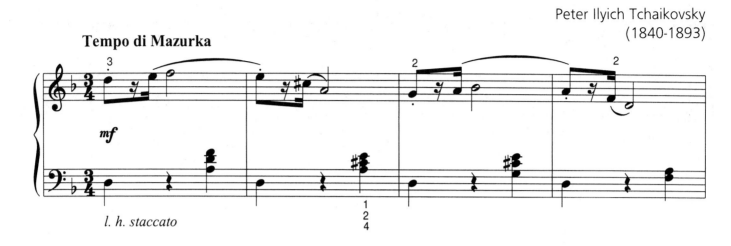

l. h. staccato

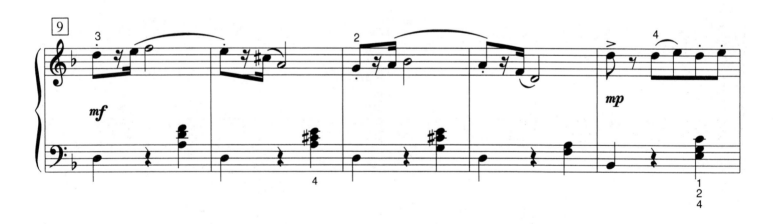

Le Petit Noir

Claude Debussy
(1862-1918)

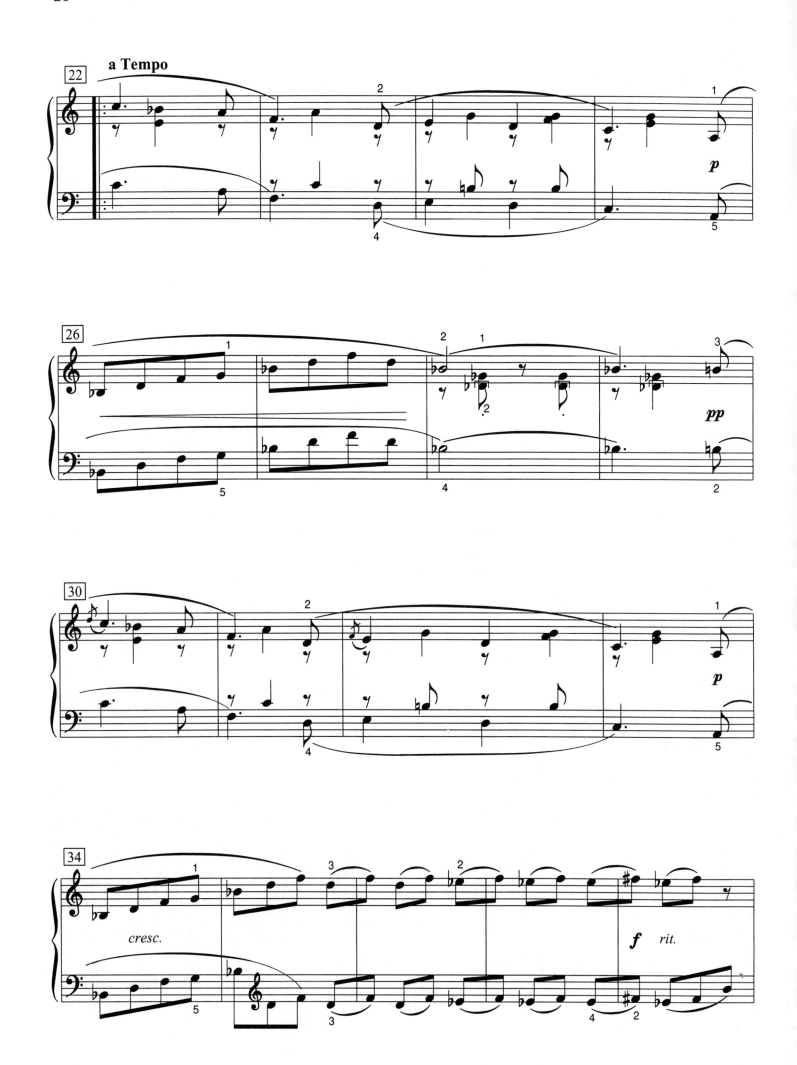

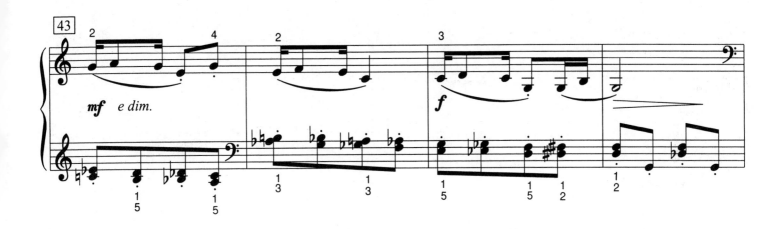

Waltz

Vladimir Rebikov
(1866-1920)

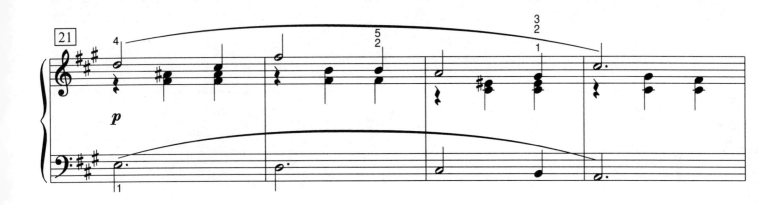

D.C. al Fine

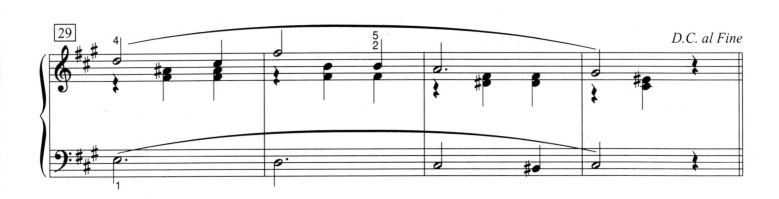

Evening in the Country

From *Ten Easy Pieces*

Béla Bartók
(1881-1945)

The Grasshopper's Wedding

From *For Children, Vol. 1*

Béla Bartók
(1881-1945)

A Little Joke

Op. 27, No. 13

Dmitri Kabalevsky
(1904-1987)

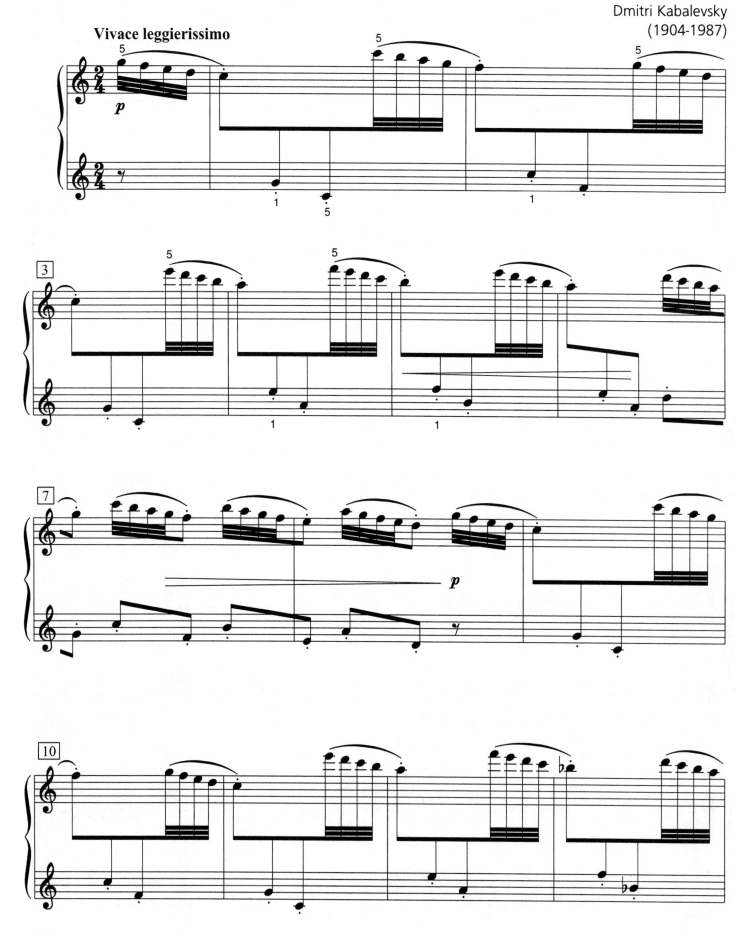

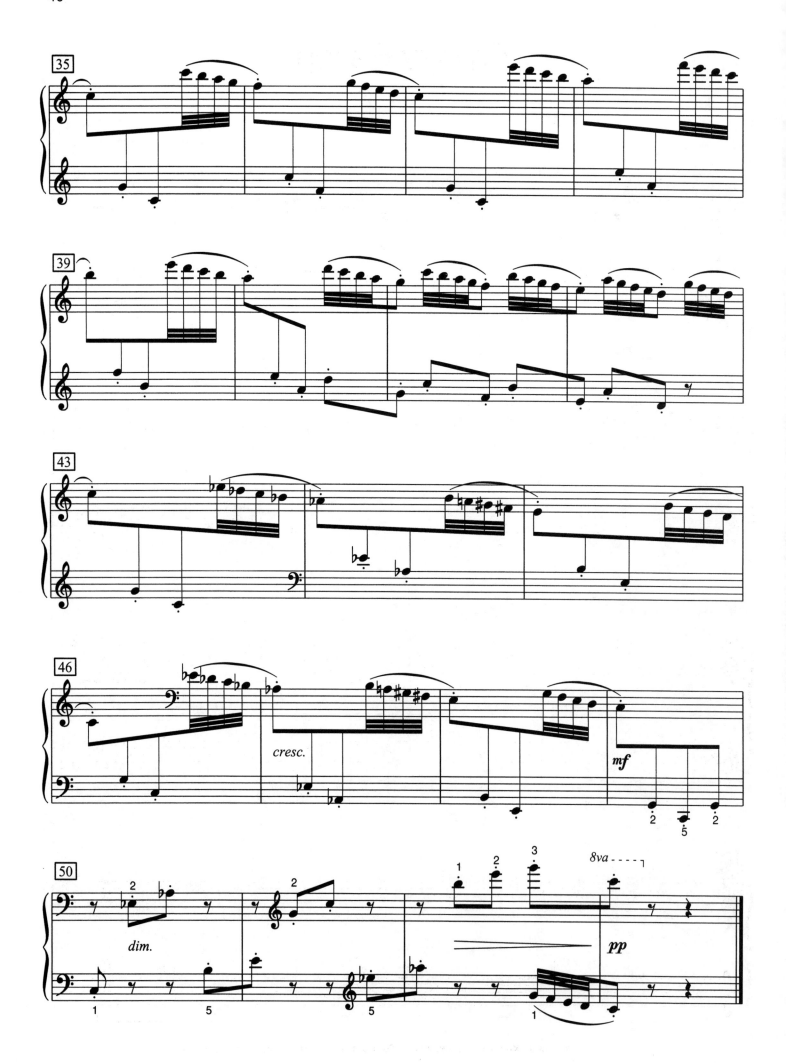

Cavalry Gallop

Op. 27, No. 29

Dmitri Kabalevsky
(1904-1987)

Allegro molto

© 1997 Neil A. Kjos Music Company, 4380 Jutland Drive, San Diego, California, 92117.

A Short Story

Op. 27, No. 20

Dmitri Kabalevsky
(1904-1987)

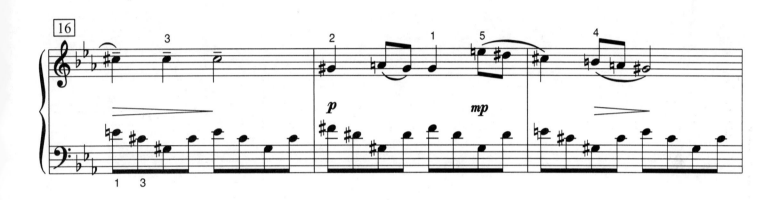

Novelette

Op. 27, No. 25

Dmitri Kabalevsky
(1904-1987)

A Warlike Dance

Op. 27, No. 19

Dmitri Kabalevsky
(1904-1987)

GP625

COMPOSER BIOGRAPHIES

Béla Bartók (1881-1945), Hungarian composer, studied piano with his mother as a child. He completed his musical training at the Franz Liszt Academy in Budapest with a pupil of Liszt. Bartók was a brilliant pianist, and he made concert tours throughout Europe and to America in 1927. He returned to Budapest where he was a Professor of Piano at the Conservatory. He came to the United States in 1940 where he lived until his death. He spent many years collecting and recording Hungarian and Rumanian folk music, much of which is reflected in his compositions. He wrote more than one hundred pieces for students. Other works include advanced piano music, orchestral works, concertos, choral music, chamber music, songs, and music for the stage.

Friedrich Burgmüller (1806-1874), German composer, came from a musical family. He moved to Paris in 1832 where he enjoyed a considerable reputation as a pianist, composer, and piano teacher. Burgmüller is particularly noted for his three sets of etudes for piano: Op. 100, Op. 105, and Op. 109.

Frédéric Chopin (1810-1849), born in Poland, lived most of his life in Paris, France. He was a child prodigy at the piano (some say that his talent rivaled that of Mozart). By the time he was twenty, he had already written fifty works for the piano. Chopin was dedicated to writing music for the piano and rarely composed for any other instrument. He wrote over two-hundred works for the piano during his lifetime. His piano music is often regarded as the most thoroughly pianistic music ever written.

Claude Debussy (1862-1918), French composer and pianist, is regarded as the creator of the Impressionist period in music. Influenced by many non-western musical styles, Debussy introduced a style of composition which included the use of Oriental pentatonic scales, the whole-tone scale, consecutive parallel chords and intervals, unresolved harmonies, and the abandonment of traditional form. He was also influenced by the sound of American Jazz which is evident in *Le Petit Noir* and *Golliwogg's Cakewalk*. His large output of piano music includes two books of *Preludes*, two books of *Etudes*, and many suites including *Estampes, Images, Suite bergamasque* (which includes the famous *Clair de lune*), and *Pour le piano*. He also wrote songs, instrumental music, and many works for orchestra.

Edvard Grieg (1843-1907), born in Bergen, Norway, was a famous pianist and composer during his lifetime. His writing style is unique for its use of Norwegian folksong. His most frequently performed works are the *Lyric Pieces* for Piano, and the *Piano Concerto in A Minor*. Grieg also wrote many works for orchestra including the suite *Peer Gynt*.

Dmitri Kabalevsky (1904-1987), Russian composer, began to play the piano by ear when he was six years old, but he did not begin formal lessons until he was fourteen. When he was twenty-one he entered the Moscow Conservatory and was such a brilliant student that upon graduation he was invited to become Professor of Composition. In addition to composing and teaching, Kabalevsky was a conductor, music critic, musicologist, and toured as a pianist. He wrote many different kinds of music: symphonies, concertos, ballets, chamber music, advanced piano pieces, and also music for radio, movies, and stage plays.